Praise fo

"Patrick Galvin's parable is a fresh take on the topic of building deep and strategic relationships grounded in trust. By thinking through the experiences of the main character, business leaders gain a unique perspective that allows them to challenge assumptions and initiate important conversations."
— Paul Witkay, founder and CEO, Alliance of Chief Executives

"The faster things change, the more important relationships become. In the future, trust will be vital to the success of every company on the planet and the lessons in this parable are core to the success of every team."
— Steve Brown, former chief evangelist and futurist for Intel; keynote speaker; author of *The Innovation Ultimatum*

"This short, entertaining story provides a compelling and time-tested way for leaders to build a lasting business on a firm foundation of trust."
— Steve Stogner, president and CEO, Grange Insurance Association

"It's not enough to have professional connections, you need connections built on trust. In this brilliant follow-up to *The Connector's Way*, Patrick Galvin outlines a simple framework to build the crucial element of trust among friends and colleagues."
— David Burkus, author of *Friend of a Friend*

"This easy to read, concise book helps you realize the significance of relationships. Good ideas and individual performance will never take you as far or be as rewarding if you do not invest in the relationships with those around you."
— Craig A. Wanichek, president and CEO, Summit Bank

"In the sequel to *The Connector's Way*, Patrick Galvin shines a much-needed spotlight on the human tendency to take shortcuts when the answer is always to do right by others."
— Richard Fenton, author, *Go For No!*

"Patrick Galvin's book on trust should be standard business school reading. But why stop at business school? *The Trusted Way* is an invaluable primer for life and decision making."
— Mike Faith, founder and CEO, Headsets.com, Inc.

"*The Trusted Way* is profound in its simplicity and relevancy to life's challenges and opportunities. The author's definition of success is more than material wealth. It is the wealth of relationships, philanthropy, and service played out using the ethical compass of The Four-Way Test."
— Al Jubitz, president, Jubitz Family Foundation; founding chair of the Rotary Action Group for Peace

"*The Trusted Way* is a gift embedded with wisdom from a character who has listened, learned, and now shared what it takes to live a meaningful life of purpose."
— Alec Horley, CFP, president and owner, Accumulus Wealth Management

"*The Trusted Way* is an approachable reminder that concepts that have been with us for many years continue to be relevant."
— Matt Shekoyan, vice president of strategy, Sunkist Growers

"*The Trusted Way* gives entrepreneurs the simplest path to building a legacy business. In a world built on people and relationships, this foundational read offers a new perspective on leveling up."
— Chris Suarez, founder and CEO, Xperience Real Estate Network

"Short, concise, and packed with pearls of wisdom, *The Trusted Way* can improve relationships and circumstances in business, personal, and family life."
— Jim Boyle, Rotary District 5100 Governor

THE TRUSTED WAY

THE
TRUSTED
WAY

**A STORY ABOUT BUILDING A LIFE
AND BUSINESS OF CHARACTER**

PATRICK
GALVIN

JRP

JOSEPH RUDOLPH PUBLISHERS • PORTLAND, OREGON

The Trusted Way: A Story About Building a Life and Business of Character
Copyright ©2021 Patrick Galvin. All rights reserved.

Published by Joseph Rudolph Publishers
www.josephrudolphpublishers.com

Library of Congress Cataloging-in-Publication Data is on file with the publisher.

ISBN   978-0-9828680-0-3 trade paperback
eISBN   978-0-9828680-1-0 electronic book

The Four-Way Test referred to in this book was created by Herbert J. Taylor in 1932 and adopted by Rotary International in 1943. Now in the public domain, The Four-Way Test is used by organizations and individuals worldwide.

Editing: Kari Filburn
Cover and book design: Ranilo Cabo

Printed in the United States of America
First printing

To my wife Ellen and daughter Anya, who trusted that the time I spent writing this book was worthwhile. Your encouragement and love mean the world to me.

Contents

Preface

Zig Ziglar, one of my favorite professional speakers, said, "If people like you, they'll listen to you, but if people trust you, they'll do business with you."[1] His quote perfectly captures my motivation for writing this book and my wish for you.

My first business parable, *The Connector's Way: A Story About Building Business One Relationship at a Time*, shared strategies, ideas, and tips for cultivating better personal and professional relationships. I have loved hearing from readers around the world about the positive impact that *The Connector's Way* has made on their lives. When a large publishing company in Beijing released the Chinese-language edition of *The Connector's Way*, I knew that I had addressed a universal need.

The advice in *The Connector's Way* for building a relationship-centric business is as true and applicable now as it was when the book was first published. However, success is ultimately dependent upon the ability of people and companies to build trust with

---

1   Kevin Miller and Tom Ziglar (hosts), "Building Trust," *The Ziglar Show*, March 16, 2015, audio, 15:47, https://www.stitcher.com/show/the-ziglar-show/episode/309-build-ing-trust-39422091.

their customers, prospects, colleagues, and referral partners. While I touched on this in *The Connector's Way*, the fundamental importance of trust motivated me to write *The Trusted Way*.

This book chronicles the journey of Brad Parsons, a young entrepreneur who went from failure to success thanks to The Four-Way Test, a simple yet powerful standard of ethics that a diverse group of mentors brings to life. In the interest of privacy, I have changed the names of the characters who are all based on real people from my life as a business owner and a Rotarian. In fact, much of the wisdom that Brad learns mirrors what I have gained from being an active member of Rotary International, one of the oldest and largest service organizations in the world. Rotarians have been unfailingly generous in sharing their stories about how focusing on trust has benefited them both personally and professionally.

In today's fast-paced world, it is tempting to look for shortcuts. But there are no quick paths to achieving lasting fame or fortune. The only sure way to success is to develop and nurture solid relationships that are grounded in trust.

It is my fervent hope that this book both inspires and equips you to follow the trusted way to the top!

Patrick Galvin
patrick@galvanizinggroup.com

1

The Winner

Brad felt his heart pound as the stage manager adjusted his over-the-ear microphone. As he waited to be announced, the advice that his college speech and debate coach gave him before every competition ran through his head: Take the stage with confidence. Watch your body language. Pause to emphasize key points. Make eye contact and smile.

"It gives me great pleasure to introduce Brad Parsons, a second-year MBA student representing the final team in this year's Entrepreneurial Challenge," announced Professor Ricardo Marquez to the crowded university auditorium filled with over six hundred students and members of the public. Professor Marquez taught Start-Up Launch, the business school's most popular course. "Brad will share his team's idea for changing the way people shop for home-service providers."

Brad strode onto the stage with a smile as the audience applauded. The spotlight shone so brightly on him that he could barely make out faces beyond the first few rows. Brad had long dreamed about this moment. Growing up as the only child of a divorced grocery store clerk who had to scrimp to make ends meet, he always knew that he wanted more from life. Ever since he could remember, he had told his mother that he was going to be rich and famous—and winning this competition was a natural step in that direction.

Before speaking, Brad paused. For three seconds, he allowed himself time to enjoy his moment in the spotlight. Then he smiled broadly and began a fifteen-minute presentation that he had practiced so many times that he had lost count. His words flowed eloquently, and his five teammates looked excitedly at each other as they watched the panel of judges in the mezzanine nodding their heads in agreement while taking copious notes. Ravi Dass, the team's chief financial officer, admired how Brad was able to explain the financial plan that they had struggled for months to create in such a clear and concise way. His teammates, like the audience, were transfixed with Brad's passion, intelligence, and confidence.

"In conclusion," Brad said, "while other consumer-review websites in the home-services space rely on text-centric content, we will feature unbiased video and audio reviews from a community of people sharing their opinions about the plumbers, electricians, remodelers, cleaners, and other service professionals that they've hired for their home projects. As most homeowners now enjoy extremely fast Internet speeds, it is high time that they be able to access reviews that are presented in a compelling way. Our dynamic content will deliver tremendous opportunities for our customers, investors, and employees. We are confident that we will revolutionize the way people choose home-service providers."

Then, unlike the other presenters who had concluded with "thank you," Brad bowed slightly toward the audience. Remembering the advice of his speech coach, he clasped his hands together in front of his chest in a demonstration of confidence, humility, and gratitude. With that, the audience burst into an applause that was louder than it had been for any other speaker. Brad smiled broadly, but he wasn't surprised. After all, his team had the best idea, the best plan—and the best presentation.

Waiting backstage were Brad's teammates, who high-fived him when he appeared behind the curtain. Ravi gave Brad a giant bear hug. "Man, that was awesome! It was even better than last night's dress rehearsal." The others nodded in agreement.

"Yeah, it was," said Brad. Brad's tone did not surprise his team members since extreme confidence was his modus operandi. Yet Ravi could not help feeling irritated that Brad hadn't shared any of the glory with the group. They had *all* put in long nights making sure that the project and presentation were perfect.

A Frustrating Homecoming

Brad smiled as he shifted his BMW convertible into high gear. Accelerating through the curves, he took in a deep breath. The fragrance of the car's fine leather mixed with the familiar pine scent coming through the open windows. It was a scent that he knew well from having grown up nearby.

His argument with Ravi, now the CFO of their start-up, Homestar Ratings, seemed like a distant memory. Brad was convinced that Ravi and the rest of the leadership team would eventually see things his way. After all, investors needed to picture him, a twenty-five-year-old president and CEO who looked even younger than his age, as the personification of success. So why shouldn't he use a small portion of the $75,000 prize from the Entrepreneurial Challenge to lease a luxury car and buy designer clothes?

Brad was so lost in his thoughts about how to furnish the company's new downtown loft space that he had to brake hard to avoid missing the exit that he knew well. About three-quarters of a mile away, on a potholed access road next to the highway, stood the Cloud Villa Mobile Home Park.

Nothing had changed. As he drove down a gravel road shaped like a horseshoe, he recognized the dented sides and faded paint on the thirty mobile homes, none of which had moved in decades. "Wow," he thought, "how can anyone possibly be satisfied living this way?"

Brad pulled up to a small gray one-bedroom mobile home that matched the dreariness of the surrounding environment. Sandra Parsons, who had heard the approaching hum of the BMW, waved from a rickety wood porch propped up next to the front door. "Welcome home, sweetie," she called out in her friendly southern drawl.

Brad pulled into the driveway behind his mother's twenty-year-old beat-up Ford pickup truck. He jumped out of the convertible, grabbed the fine leather overnight bag from his back seat, and bounded up the uneven wood steps to hug his mother.

"You're even more handsome than I remember." His mother grinned. "Come on in, I just made a fresh pitcher of sweet tea. You must be thirsty after the drive."

Brad settled into the soft floral-print loveseat in the front of the mobile home. His mother hummed quietly to herself in the kitchen as she poured the sweet tea and arranged a plate of key lime cookies.

Returning to the sitting area, Sandra breathlessly updated Brad on the lives of the Cloud Villa Mobile

Home Park residents before moving on to stories about the townspeople she thought Brad would remember.

Brad tried to feign interest. His mother's catalog of stories about people he did not care about was one of the many things that annoyed him about visiting. He already regretted that he had told her that he would spend the weekend.

"Honey," his mother asked, "am I boring you?" Brad's unenthusiastic "no" didn't fool her. She pivoted the conversation to something that had caused her to lose sleep over the past few weeks.

She asked, "Did you hear that Wegman's closed two months ago? They couldn't compete with the low prices of the superstore that moved into Mapleton."

For Sandra, this was big news. She had been a cashier at the only grocery store in town for fifteen years. There were only a handful of other retailers nearby, so getting a new grocery position would be difficult.

"It's not me that I'm worried about," said Sandra by way of reassurance. "I've picked up a few regular housekeeping jobs to pay the bills. Plus, the trailer is paid off—and I'm the world's best coupon cutter."

A worried look quickly replaced Sandra's smile.

"Your cousins aren't as lucky. Since losing their jobs at Wegman's, they haven't found new work. Ray's wife is due in about a month, and things are especially tough because they already have three mouths to feed.

"I was hoping that you might be able to help Ray's family out until he finds something. I've been doing what I can, but I just don't have enough to provide what they need."

Brad could not believe what he was hearing. His mother was dipping into her own scarce resources to help his cousin. "You need to cut Ray off," snapped Brad. "He needs to get out of his recliner and find a job."

"Honey, there just isn't a lot of work out there right now," implored Sandra. "Ray is trying, but—"

Brad interrupted his mother. "I've been here for ten minutes, and you're already leaning on me to come to Ray's rescue," he said with a raised voice. "Why should I help him? It's not my fault that he dropped out of high school and can't get his act together."

Brad stood abruptly and grabbed his overnight bag.

"I can't deal with this," he said as he strode toward the door. "Now I remember why I don't visit—you and everybody else here never stops asking for things."

A few seconds later, Sandra heard the squeal of the BMW's tires as it peeled out of the trailer park.

Getting Ready

Brad felt a momentary pang of guilt for the way he had ended things with his mother. While he was bothered about being asked to support his cousin, he had used his mother's request as an excuse to abruptly end a trip that he had never wanted to make in the first place.

Brad had far bigger priorities to deal with.

The angel investors who had put over $3 million into Homestar Ratings based on its first-place finish in the prestigious Entrepreneurial Challenge were growing frustrated with the company's continued underperformance. The strength of the company's business plan and Brad's repeated promises that profitability was around the corner did nothing to temper their concerns.

Brad had spent the ninety-minute drive home thinking about his upcoming slide presentation to update investors. Fortunately, he knew the road well. He had taken it every day for four years when he commuted from the trailer park to the state college where he had earned his undergraduate business degree.

Brad was confident that the company's 50 percent revenue jump in the last quarter—which the angel investors didn't know about yet—would not only save his position as president and CEO but also pave the way for another round of desperately needed venture funding.

After a brief stop at a convenience store to pick up a high-energy drink, Brad sped to his condo and sprinted up the stairs from the garage to his fifteenth-floor penthouse loft with a picturesque view of the city's skyline. Energized and caffeinated, Brad spent the rest of the weekend feverishly working on a slide presentation to highlight the company's recent growth and prove that it would beat its annual revenue forecast. He was sure that his angel investors would jump at the chance to participate in a new round of venture funding that he needed to keep the company afloat.

On Sunday night, with his slides finished, Brad practiced his thirty-minute presentation five times until he collapsed in exhaustion. Sitting in a lounge chair in his home office with its floor-to-ceiling windows, he looked out at the twinkling skyline. Then, as he always did before a big presentation, he shut his eyes and visualized himself delivering an eloquent speech to an enraptured audience.

As the audience's imaginary compliments filled his head, Brad drifted off into a deep sleep.

Unwelcome Surprise

At 5 a.m., Brad's smartphone played Queen's "We Are the Champions," his morning wake-up alarm since college. The song had unfailingly irritated all his roommates over the years, but Brad didn't care. It always energized him.

He leapt out of the chair where he had spent the night and darted into the kitchen to gulp down a cup of water with lemon juice. Hydrated, he went into the living room, which doubled as a workout space, and turned on his favorite high-intensity interval training workout. The livestream played on an enormous television mounted on a brick wall with surround sound from eight speakers.

After an intense workout, he returned to the kitchen for his favorite breakfast: steel-cut oatmeal, dried fruits, and walnuts, washed down with a large cup of dark-roast coffee combined with grass-fed butter and coconut oil. Popularized on social media, the concoction had become his favorite morning jolt after a late night of working or partying.

Wanting to beat traffic, Brad showered briskly. Although he had spent a small fortune renovating his bathroom with a luxurious rainfall shower, he had yet to fully enjoy it. He toweled off quickly, combed sculpting cream through his hair, and brushed his teeth with a mint toothpaste that he had picked up during a stay at London's fanciest hotel. On that trip, he had also purchased an elegant bespoke suit, which he chose to wear for his big presentation that morning.

Brad used the short drive to the office to visualize how the day would unfold, from impressing his investors with his presentation to celebrating with employees at his favorite whiskey bar at the end of the workday.

As he turned into the parking lot, Brad was surprised to see four sedans parked in the visitor section. "Since when," he wondered, "did my investors decide to color coordinate their cars?"

Brad pulled his BMW convertible into the spot marked PRESIDENT/CEO. He hopped out, feeling excited about what lay ahead. Walking into the front lobby, with its soaring glass windows and sleek marble reception desk, Brad was thrown off by the sight of eight men dressed alike. They wore khakis, white shirts, and blue windbreakers with yellow lettering.

"Mr. Parsons?" asked the tallest of the men.

"Yes, that's me," replied Brad.

"We're from the US Marshals Service Office, and we have a warrant for your arrest and the seizure of company documents," said Officer James Walsh.

"What? Is this some kind of joke that my CFO, Ravi, cooked up? I don't think it's funny," said Brad. "Especially on a day like today."

"No, this is real," said Walsh, handing him the arrest warrant and supporting legal documents.

Brad scanned the list of charges. "Clearly, you've made a huge mistake."

In a serious and monotone voice, Walsh replied, "Mr. Parsons, you have the right to remain silent. Anything you say can and will be used against you in a court of law. You have the right to an attorney. If you cannot afford an attorney, one will be provided for you."

Brad barely heard the officer as he finished reading him his rights. He felt like he was trapped in a bad dream. Surely, he would wake up any minute and it would all be over.

"Please give me your cell phone and extend your hands out, palms facing downward," said Walsh calmly. The metal handcuffs snapped shut with a loud click. With his serious-looking associates leading the way, Walsh put a firm arm around Brad's shoulders and guided him out of the lobby and toward one of the black sedans.

Sitting in the back seat behind a plexiglass partition, Brad listened to Walsh instruct his team to return to the building and seize all the documents in the executive suite, along with all smartphones and computers.

Feeling like the floor had fallen out from under him, Brad turned to look out the window and saw Ravi crossing the parking lot on his way toward the lobby. Their eyes met momentarily, and Brad saw Ravi mouth, "What's going on?"

Brad averted his gaze and sank down in his seat.

5

The Plea

A ray of sunshine shone through the window onto Brad's face, waking him up after a fitful night's sleep. Opening his eyes, he took in his surroundings. The small, dingy single-occupancy cell was lit by an overhead fluorescent light, and the metal bed built into the wall was covered with a threadbare mattress.

He stood up to stretch his shoulders and back. Accustomed to the expensive memory foam mattress at his loft, he felt achy and sore. He was also angry at being treated like a common criminal. The strong smell of body odor from the previous occupant made him feel sick to his stomach.

He heard the creaky wheels of a rolling cart stop outside his cell. Then a tray holding a cup of coffee, a banana, a bowl of corn flakes, and a carton of milk was pushed through a grate at the bottom of the door. Brad looked at the bland meal with disinterest and lay back down on the bed to wait for his attorney's 9 a.m. arrival.

"Get up, Parsons!" shouted the guard as he knocked loudly on the door. Then he flung it open so that it banged against the wall. "Your lawyer is here."

Brad jumped up from the bed, ran his fingers through his matted hair, and smoothed down the creases in his orange jumpsuit. Following the guard down the hallway, he was guided into a small room with a metal table and two chairs. The guard instructed him to sit down and wait.

Ten minutes later, the door opened. The guard ushered his attorney A. J. Wilkins, a short, balding middle-aged man dressed in a conservative dark suit, into the room.

"Hello, Brad," greeted Wilkins. "I'm sorry that I couldn't meet with you yesterday, but I couldn't delay the deposition that I had already scheduled. Good news, though. I've worked out a bail arrangement with the judge."

"That's great," said Brad. "But what about getting these ridiculous charges dismissed?"

"Ah . . . I wish it were that easy," replied Wilkins. "But the Federal Trade Commission's investigation into your company was exhaustive. The evidence that they've presented for false advertising, customer extortion, and defrauding investors appears quite credible."

Brad felt his blood pressure rise and his face flush. "I read the evidence file, too," he lashed out. "They did find some things at Homestar that shouldn't have been done, but I wasn't involved in any of them."

Brad's proclamation of innocence sounded familiar. Wilkins had heard it many times over in his twenty-year legal career as one of the city's most successful white-collar defense attorneys.

Wilkins listened as Brad spent the next fifteen minutes complaining about the unfair accusations against him. He knew that Brad, like the other clients he represented, needed to vent before being receptive to his counsel.

"I know that you're upset," said Wilkins as Brad wound down. "And you might well be innocent of some, if not all, of the charges. However, the FTC's investigation is well constructed. The texts, emails, and voice messages on your cell phone are incriminating."

"I don't care," countered Brad. "I will not go down without a fight. We can win this."

Wilkins remained calm. "Naturally, I would represent you in a trial. But you should know that your defense will be expensive. If we lose, which is probably a 50 percent chance, you'll likely face a ten-to-fifteen-year felony sentence in a federal penitentiary—with no parole opportunity for at least six to seven years."

Stunned into silence, Brad stared at Wilkins. He shook his head from side to side, as if trying to wake himself from a nightmare. "Do I have any good alternatives?" he asked quietly.

"Actually, you do," answered Wilkins.

6

The Sentence

A week after posting bail, Brad lay in bed, wide awake at 4:30 a.m. He felt like he was going crazy. The monotony of days spent reviewing the FTC's detailed charges and his legal options was taking a toll. The uncertainty of what lay ahead was causing him to lose sleep, and he didn't have the energy to eat right or exercise. The 8 a.m. video conference call with his attorney could not come fast enough.

"How are you holding up under home confinement?" asked Wilkins from a pop-up window that filled half of Brad's computer screen.

"Not well," mumbled a bleary-eyed Brad. "I'm having a hard time keeping it together. The charges make me seem like a criminal when all I did was drive my team hard. They were expected to boost revenue, but I *never* told them to push home-service providers to pay for positive reviews or for greater visibility on our website.

"I don't know whether Ravi or the other account executives were involved. I can't imagine why they would have done it except to maximize their commissions—"

"Here's the thing," interrupted Wilkins. "We may never know why your team members did what they did. But we can't waste our time with this now. The FTC will drop the felony charges against you if you are willing to plea to lesser misdemeanor counts and pay a fine of $250,000."

"That sounds better than I had imagined," said Brad as he perked up for the first time in a week.

"Well, there's one more thing to consider. In lieu of serving time in a federal penitentiary, you must agree to ninety days of home confinement," replied Wilkins.

As soon as Brad heard these words, the skin on his right ankle where his GPS tracker was located began to feel hot. The thought of having to wear the uncomfortable device that had been put on him when he left the federal courthouse was unbearable.

"No way. I'll pay the fine and agree to home confinement, but I won't wear this painful device anymore."

Exasperated, Wilkins responded, "Sorry, Brad, you don't get to pick your sentence like you are ordering at a steak house. You are lucky that you even have a home-confinement option. You're only getting it because you are a first-time offender and prisons are overcrowded."

Brad sighed in defeat. "Okay, but if I agree to wear the GPS tracker, can I get the home confinement waived?"

"Not a chance," said Wilkins. "We can't push it, Brad. We need to act while the FTC is willing to deal, and ninety days is a remarkably short sentence for home confinement. What do you want me to do?"

"Take the deal," said Brad glumly.

Brad ended the conference call and opened his email. He felt his stomach drop as he saw a message from Ravi with the subject line "Board of Directors Decision." He took a deep breath and clicked on the message.

> *Brad,*
>
> *It is my duty to inform you that the board of directors held an emergency meeting yesterday and made the unanimous decision to terminate you as president and CEO of Homestar Ratings given the serious charges you face. This is effective immediately. Your personal items have been packed and will be delivered to your home via courier service on Monday.*
>
> *Per the terms of your employment, a valuation process of your equity stake has been authorized and should take four to six weeks to complete. Once the process has been completed, you will receive full payment for your shares and will be fully divested of any financial interest in Homestar Ratings.*
> *Sincerely,*
> *Ravi Dass, CFO/Interim President*

Brad's face flushed red in anger at the thought that his best friend had stabbed him in the back.

7

Home Confinement

To Brad's surprise, the first few weeks of his ninety-day home confinement passed by quickly. He fell into a daily routine of waking up at 7 a.m., weightlifting for thirty minutes, and pedaling furiously on his high-tech stationary bike. He was determined to maintain his place atop the leaderboard for the most calories burned in his online cycling class.

His workout complete, Brad filled his mornings by scanning news websites and hosting virtual coffee meetings with former employees and friends from business school. He spent his afternoons writing articles for his blog, in which he shared his personal opinions and predictions on what was happening in the business world.

As an excellent writer whose legal troubles had received widespread media attention, Brad soon began to build an online following that generated thousands of views. Just a few weeks into his sentence, he was receiving daily interview requests from business reporters and podcast hosts whose audiences were curious to hear what he had to say.

Brad also became a voracious reader, spending three to four hours a day reading the autobiographies of successful entrepreneurs and devouring books about business start-ups and socially responsible enterprises. Brad knew that he wanted to start another company, and he was sure that his writing and reading would provide him with an idea of what his next business should be.

As busy as his activities kept him, Brad felt lonely for the first time in his adult life. Per the judge's orders, he couldn't even make a trip to the grocery store. Instead, delivery people brought his groceries to the front door. Nobody ever stopped long enough to chat.

To combat his loneliness, Brad spent evenings scrolling through dating apps on his smartphone. Focused on building his company, he had not dated much since graduating from business school. Now, he was excited to give it another try.

Brad certainly didn't have any difficulties attracting interest from the opposite sex. His wavy blond hair, deep-blue eyes, and distinctive square jaw inspired an impressive number of clicks on his profile. His educational and business background—which conveniently omitted his misdemeanor conviction—also set him apart.

Used to the attention, Brad wasn't surprised when his inbox quickly filled up with messages from admirers. But he was never interested in the women who were attracted to him. Instead, he always seemed to be on the hunt for something (or someone) more.

Midway through his home confinement, Brad was scrolling through dating profile photos when Sally Elkins' radiant smile and bright-red hair caught his eye. Intrigued, Brad clicked on her profile. He was delighted to see that in her biography, Sally talked mostly about her business dreams and goals.

"I like her priorities," thought Brad. Immediately, he fired off a message—and then sat back and waited.

The few times that Brad had taken the initiative to reach out to dating prospects, he had always heard back in a few hours. When three days passed without a response from Sally, however, he assumed that she was no longer available. So, he was surprised to receive a message from Sally while livestreaming his new podcast.

Really enjoying your show. Let's talk soon.

Brad was in the middle of an interview with his favorite business school professor who was also one of the world's leading branding experts. He had spent weeks trying to arrange a videoconference with the busy professor who travelled around the world keynoting at conferences and consulting with large corporations. As interested as he was in hearing what the professor had to say, Brad was suddenly preoccupied.

What would he say to the elusive Sally when he finally talked to her?

8

The Prelude

Thanking the professor for being a guest on his show, Brad took off his headset and went to the kitchen to grab an ice-cold bottle of beer. He made his way out to the balcony, where the late-October sun was just starting to set against the city skyline.

Reclining on his favorite lounge chair, Brad texted Sally.

Sorry for the delayed response. How are you?

Sally's response came quickly.

Loved your show and the professor's branding ideas! He gave me a lot to think about as I try to grow my business.

Brad smiled. She was as focused on business as he was.

What is it that you do?

His phone pinged back.

I prefer talking to texting. How about a video chat?

Seconds later, Brad's phone vibrated with an incoming video call. He accepted the call, and Sally's smiling face appeared.

Brad was instantly smitten. Even on a small screen, there was something electric about Sally's presence. He had never felt such an immediate attraction and unconsciously began shaking his head as if to deny his thoughts.

"Why the headshake?" asked Sally.

"Sorry, I was just trying to adjust the audio in my earbuds," responded Brad, trying to sound calm. "They're working like a charm now."

Speaking for nearly an hour, Brad and Sally discovered that they had a lot in common. They both had graduated from the same business school, but Brad had finished the semester before Sally had started. They were both passionate about business, with Sally having worked for one of the city's largest commercial real-estate brokerages before deciding to go out on her own with her own commercial real-estate company. They had similar tastes in books and were the first people in their families to go to college. Neither had dated much in the past couple of years because they were too busy pursuing their entrepreneurial dreams.

Sally finally said, "It's getting late. I need to get ready for a big meeting with a developer tomorrow. How about meeting for lunch downtown sometime this week?"

Brad halted. "I would love to," he said. "There's just one small problem with that idea."

"Oh, what's that?" asked Sally.

While he had considered inventing an excuse for not being able to meet with her, Brad knew that Sally would eventually find out about his situation. A lie would end any chance he had with Sally. So, he took a deep breath and shared the story of the wrongful charges and his confinement.

For five minutes, Sally listened intently. As he wrapped up, Brad expected that Sally would have a lot of questions for him. Instead, she stared blankly into the screen for what seemed like an eternity. After a few seconds, she responded softly and without emotion: "I didn't expect that. Let me think about things, and I'll get back to you."

With that, Sally's image flicked off the screen.

9

Too Good to Be True

Brad barely slept for the next five nights. Tossing and turning in bed, he wondered if he would ever hear from Sally again. Instead of working out, he spent his mornings trying to catch up on the sleep he had missed during the night.

On a rainy afternoon that matched his gloominess, Brad tried distracting himself with the latest Steve Jobs biography. Barely focusing on the words, he kept reading the same paragraph over and over. Suddenly, his cell phone rang loudly and jarred him from his trance-like state. Seeing Sally's name appear on the screen, he felt his heart jump. He picked up the phone.

"Hello, Brad," said Sally, rather matter-of-factly.

"Hey, Sally." Brad paced back and forth across the floor. "I'm so happy it's you. I thought that I wasn't going to hear from you again."

Sally replied, "I considered that option. I just didn't want to experience the same sort of pain."

"What do you mean?" asked Brad.

Sally cleared her throat. "My father was caught forging checks from the auto dealership where he worked when I was twelve. He claimed that he was innocent. But a jury found him guilty, and he went to prison. He got out on parole when I was fifteen. The three years that he spent in jail were terrible for my mom and me. She struggled to find a job and could barely pay for rent and food. And, when she had to apply for food stamps, she felt totally humiliated."

"Now I understand why you didn't call back," said Brad. "But I didn't do anything wrong. I only plead guilty to low-level misdemeanor charges so the company and I could move on without incurring huge legal debts."

There was a momentary silence. Then Sally asked, "Do you swear that you didn't do anything illegal?"

"I didn't do anything wrong," insisted Brad. "I swear."

"I want to believe you," said Sally. "But I'll be honest. You sound a lot like my father. My mother and I believed him when he said he was innocent. But during the trial, we found out that it was not true—and that he deserved his sentence."

"I get it. I'd be suspicious, too. You deserve to know the facts." He paused before continuing. "I was obsessed with building a profitable company, and I drove my employees and executive team hard. They took my commitment to success as justification for taking the aggressive measures that got us in trouble with the Federal Trade Commission."

"What sort of measures?" asked Sally.

"Well, my CFO, Ravi, who was my best friend from business school, developed a plan for charging advertisers for guaranteed top positions in our ranking of home-service providers, even if they didn't deserve them. He pushed our sales team to sell the new plan hard. At the same time, he was driving the marketing folks to create an expensive advertising campaign that touted Homestar Ratings as nonbiased."

"How could you not know about these things, Brad?" countered Sally. "Weren't you the president and CEO?"

"I had no idea what Ravi was doing," insisted Brad. "But when I found out, I didn't want to turn him in or get other employees in trouble because I care about them. Pleading to lesser charges just seemed like the right thing to do."

There was so much about Brad that Sally liked, and she really wanted to believe him. Yet, she couldn't push lingering doubts out of her mind. She needed the advice of somebody she could trust—and she knew the exact right person: Andrea.

"I need more time to think about things. I'll get back to you," said Sally as she hung up the phone.

10

The Trusted Advisor

On day ninety-one of his home confinement, Brad hopped out of bed feeling elated. He glanced at his watch with anticipation. In a few short hours, he would be at the courthouse to have the uncomfortable GPS tracker removed from his ankle.

Skipping breakfast, Brad took a fast shower and put on the designer jeans, black turtleneck, and high-top leather sneakers that made his signature look. Humming to himself, he admired his reflection in the mirror as he took the elevator down to the parking garage. He smiled when he saw his beloved BMW convertible. After taking a minute to wipe off the accumulated dust, he jumped in and sped out of the garage.

"This will take just a minute," said the court bailiff. He was tapping furiously on his computer keyboard as Brad watched impatiently from a chair next to the desk.

"Now, extend your leg." The bailiff entered a code on the tracking device's keypad. Its lock made a few whirring noises and the metal band released itself from Brad's sweaty ankle.

"You're good to go, Mr. Parsons," said the bailiff. "Don't forget to call your parole officer at 5 p.m. today for your daily check-in."

"Will do," said Brad as he quickly excused himself.

Brad hurriedly left the courthouse for his 10 a.m. appointment with Andrea Hanson. Andrea was Sally's insurance agent. She was also Sally's best friend—and the person whose opinion Sally trusted the most. While Brad was annoyed that Sally wanted him to meet with Andrea before agreeing to go out with him, he was willing to do whatever it took.

Around the time that Brad was at the courthouse, Andrea was online trying to learn as much as she could about Brad from news reports and social media feeds. It was a practice that she employed with prospective insurance customers to uncover shared interests and build rapport. And while Andrea was impressed with Brad's business success, she had a hard time squaring his accomplishments with the story he had told Sally.

At exactly 10 a.m., there were three quick knocks on Andrea's office door, and she went to open it. "Please come in," she said as she extended her hand to Brad. "I've been looking forward to meeting you."

Andrea returned to her desk, and Brad settled into a comfortable chair across from her. He glanced around the office with its typical décor: bookcases, framed photos and university degrees, and trophies recognizing sales achievements. There was also a championship cup belonging to the girls' soccer team that Andrea coached.

Attempting to build a connection, Brad asked Andrea about her role as a soccer coach. He only half-listened to her response, however, as he was busy thinking about the next thing he could say to impress her.

Suddenly, something caught his eye. It was a framed copy of yellow parchment paper hanging on the wall behind Andrea. Its large words written in calligraphy were easily visible from where Brad was sitting.

THE FOUR-WAY TEST
of the things we think, say, or do

1. Is it the TRUTH?
2. Is it FAIR to all concerned?
3. Will it build GOODWILL and BETTER FRIENDSHIPS?
4. Will it be BENEFICIAL to all concerned?

Tracking his gaze, Andrea said, "My grandfather gave me this document when I started my career as an insurance agent. He received it when he joined the Downtown Rotary Club in 1952."

"Small world," said Brad. "My grandfather was a Rotarian, too. But I've never heard of The Four-Way Test. What is it?"

"Well, it's an interesting story," said Andrea. "In 1932, in the depths of the Great Depression, the creditors of the Club Aluminum Products Company in Chicago asked a thirty-nine-year-old executive named Herbert J. Taylor to lead the company and save it from bankruptcy. The company, which distributed cookware and other household items, was struggling as the economy contracted and consumers cut back on spending. And while the company had excellent products and employees, many of its competitors did, too."

"So, what did Taylor do?" asked Brad, intrigued.

Andrea replied, "Taylor decided to focus on improving the character, dependability, and service mindedness of his team members. Club Aluminum had a code of ethics, but Taylor thought it was too long and unremarkable. This inspired him to come up with The Four-Way Test. It was a simple measuring stick that employees could memorize and use to make decisions and guide their actions."

"I can't believe that such a simple credo could turn a business around." Brad was unconvinced.

Andrea nodded. "That's what I thought, too. But Taylor credited The Four-Way Test with saving Club Aluminum. As people saw the company's commitment to ethics reflected in its actions, sales and referrals rose. The company was able to repay all its debts and return to profitability.

"One last thing," continued Andrea. "I have a small present for you." She walked to an armoire in the corner of her office and pulled out a coffee cup that she handed to Brad. It featured Hanson Insurance Agency's logo on one side and The Four-Way Test on the other.

With as much enthusiasm as he could muster, Brad thanked Andrea for the gift. After all, he wanted her to put in a good word about him with Sally. At the same time, he doubted that something as simple as The Four-Way Test had any relevance to him at all.

11

Awakening

Brad left Andrea's office feeling anxious, not only about the impression he had made but also for the work he had left on the business plan that he had been putting together for the duration of his home confinement.

Initially, he had thought about creating an Internet business to compete directly with Homestar Ratings. The idea of outperforming the company that had dismissed him pleased Brad's ego. But something did not feel quite right. He wanted something that gave his life a greater sense of purpose and meaning.

Brad's home confinement had given him plenty of time to reflect on his past and reexamine his values. Reluctantly, he acknowledged that he had started Homestar Ratings with one goal: to create the greatest amount of personal wealth in the shortest amount of time. He had not done anything in his life to make the world better.

During his confinement, Brad had racked his brain for new ideas. Thinking back to his college days, he remembered an elective he had taken called Socially Responsible Enterprise. At the time, his main reason for choosing it was that the professor was a notoriously easy grader—leaving Brad with more time to focus on more strategic classes like finance, accounting, and business negotiation. Much to Brad's surprise, he enjoyed the course. It taught him that a well-run, socially responsible enterprise could create more positive change in people's lives than most government programs.

He had also thought about the semester he had spent in Brazil for a study-abroad program. It was his first time out of the country, and he loved everything about the experience, from Brazil's beautiful beaches to its amazing music, food, and soccer matches. Yet, the rampant poverty in the country's poor neighborhoods, or favelas, was hard to ignore. Brad had never seen so many people who lacked access to essentials like food, proper housing, and security.

The business plan had come to him in a eureka moment: he would start a company in Brazil that would employ low-income workers at fair wages to create ultrastylish handmade sandals from recycled rubber.

Now, with his recent conversation with Andrea replaying in his head, he was laser focused on completing his financial projections and marketing plan. Brad was surprised to see that he had been working for eight solid hours. Too tired to eat dinner, much less celebrate his newfound freedom with friends, Brad made himself a cup of chamomile tea. Sipping from the mug that Andrea had given him that morning, he contemplated the twenty-four words that made up The Four-Way Test. As hard as he tried, he still couldn't understand the power of their simplicity.

Warmed by the tea, Brad was suddenly overwhelmed by sleepiness. He climbed the stairs to his bedroom and lay down on his bed, thinking he would rest for just a moment before getting up to change and brush his teeth. But within a few minutes, Brad fell into a deep slumber—and he dreamed for the first time in months.

Standing in a wide-open field, Brad felt a shadow looming over him. He looked over his shoulder to see a twenty-foot version of his new coffee mug hovering just a few feet from the ground. It was emblazoned with The Four-Way Test and sitting on its lip was an old man. His legs dangling, the old man smiled down at Brad.

"Could it really be?" thought Brad. His grandfather had died fifteen years earlier—and yet . . . here he was.

"You've grown since I last saw you, Brad," said his grandfather. Flummoxed, Brad asked his grandfather what he was doing there.

"Ignore me," he replied. "Focus on The Four-Way Test instead. I sense that you've wandered far from its wisdom."

"How would you know?" asked Brad. "Wait a minute. Are you my grandfather or my guardian angel?"

"Guardian angel, that's a good one!" His grandfather's unmistakable laugh filled Brad's ears. "Nobody needs a guardian angel to know what's right. They just need to look inward."

"I don't understand," said Brad.

"You will," said his grandfather as the light grew brighter and he faded away.

Streaming through the windows and into his eyes, the sunlight woke Brad from his sleep. He blinked, unsure of what had just happened. "What time is it?" he asked the voice-controlled speaker next to his bed.

"The time is 8 a.m.," announced the monotone female voice.

Brad had slept solidly through the night—something he had not been able to do in months.

12

The Realization

Still trying to process his dream, Brad lay in bed thinking about what Andrea had told him about Herbert J. Taylor and the Club Aluminum Products Company. Curious to learn more about The Four-Way Test, he picked up his smartphone from the nightstand. An online search revealed the following:

Created by Herbert J. Taylor in 1932, the twenty-four words of The Four-Way Test are held as the standard that Rotary Club members use to make ethical decisions and develop personal and professional relationships. Taylor granted Rotary International, the global federation of Rotary Clubs, the rights to use The Four-Way Test in the 1940s and the copyright in 1954 when he served as the organization's president. Now in the public domain, it has been translated into the languages of more than one hundred countries and is used by organizations and individuals worldwide.

His mind whirling with ideas, Brad got up and went to the living room where he pulled out his yoga mat. Not one to sit still for very long, Brad found a twelve-minute guided meditation on his smartphone's mindfulness app and pressed the play button.

With the sounds of chirping birds and rustling leaves playing in the background, a voice gently instructed, "Find a quiet space and sit comfortably on the floor or in a chair. Focus on your breath. Breathe in slowly. At the end of your inhale, say the number *one* to yourself. Breathe out slowly. At the end of your exhale, say the number *two* to yourself. Keep repeating this while feeling more and more relaxed."

Brad stayed focused for a few minutes until visions of his grandfather came surging back. As if reading his mind, the instructor said, "If your mind has wandered, that's normal. Recognize a new thought by saying 'thinking,' and then let go of it. Pretend it is a leaf that you are putting into the river so it may float away. Go back to focusing on your breathing."

When the bell sounded to signal the end of the session, Brad jumped up from his yoga mat. He headed to the kitchen, where he saw the mug that Andrea had given him—the one from his dream—on the countertop. As he prepared his usual cup of coffee, Brad felt the sudden urge to reconnect with Ravi.

Ravi was one of his oldest friends, yet Brad had not spoken with him since the day he had been arrested in the parking lot of Homestar Ratings. "Call Ravi," he instructed his smartphone's voice assistant.

"Brad, I was wondering if you would call. How are things?"

"Complicated," replied Brad. "It's hard to know what to say, even though I've rehearsed this phone call in my head many times."

"Don't overthink it," said Ravi. "What's on your mind?"

"I'm incredibly sorry to have put you and Homestar in such a bad spot," said Brad remorsefully. "I shouldn't have encouraged the sales team to pressure customers to pay for preferential listings, and I shouldn't have asked the marketing team to make claims that were not true. I was wrong, and I alone deserve the blame."

For a moment, Ravi was speechless. For months, Brad and his attorneys had vehemently denied any wrongdoing.

"Wow," he managed to say. "I wasn't expecting this from you. Why the 180?" asked Ravi.

Brad spent the next ten minutes updating Ravi on everything that had happened since that fateful day in the parking lot: meeting Sally, being introduced to Andrea, learning about The Four-Way Test, and seeing his grandfather in a dream. Ravi's surprise was doubled when Brad, at the end of his monologue, invited him to join him as cofounder of the socially responsible shoe company that he was starting.

As impressive as Brad's detailed business plan sounded, Ravi hesitated. He didn't recognize this new Brad, the one who suddenly cared about moral character and personal relationships.

"Listen, Brad," said Ravi. "I'm glad you are committed to running a business the right way. But I can't just walk away from Homestar because people here depend on me. And to be totally honest, I need to see that your commitment is more than simply words."

13

The Start-Up

Brad worked relentlessly for the next several months to turn All Good, his socially responsible shoe company—named after the English translation of the popular Brazilian phrase *tudo bem*—into a start-up success. He leveraged his Portuguese-speaking ability and understanding of Brazilian culture to build strong relationships. He found a manufacturing partner that hired and trained inexperienced workers and believed in promoting from within—providing an unusual opportunity for previously low-skilled workers to rise into management ranks.

Importantly, the factory's business practices were aligned with The Four-Way Test, which had guided Brad since the night his grandfather had appeared to him in a dream. The factory owner, Helio Soares, was an active member of the local Rotary Club in Brazil and had invited Brad to join him at one of the club's weekly meetings. It was there that Brad had seen a banner of The Four-Way Test, translated into Portuguese, prominently displayed at the front of the meeting room. And it was because of their shared values that Brad, who was bootstrapping All Good's growth from his savings, was able to negotiate extended payment terms with Helio.

Brad's hard work began to pay off when All Good's stylish and socially responsible footwear started attracting attention in the fashion press and from social media influencers. Scrambling to keep up with demand, Brad reconnected with Nancy Tuckerman, the business school professor whose Socially Responsible Enterprise class had left such an indelible impression. The first five employees he hired were all former students of Professor Tuckerman.

As happy as Brad was with the company's growth, he knew that he needed the advice and experience of more seasoned professionals. He fired off one of the most important texts of his life.

Hey, Ravi, do you have 15 minutes for a video call?

The response was swift.

Yes, call me in five.

This time, the conversation went very differently. Ravi had been following the stories in the business press about Brad's new socially conscious venture and admired its success. In the interim, a large Internet conglomerate had purchased Homestar Ratings, and the company had become too bureaucratic and slow growing for Ravi. It was the right time for him to leave.

A week later, Ravi was sitting on the balcony of Brad's penthouse. The chance to become an equity partner and president of All Good while Brad retained the CEO title was an opportunity that Ravi could not pass up. They celebrated their partnership—as well as the company's first million-dollar revenue month—with a bottle of champagne.

"I'm thinking about putting together a board of advisors to make sure that we stay on track," said Brad. "What do you think?"

"That's a great idea." said Ravi. "Who do you want to have on the board?"

"Well, definitely Professor Tuckerman," said Brad. He knew that Ravi would remember her since he had taken the Socially Responsible Enterprise class with him at business school.

"I also want to ask our insurance advisor, Andrea Hanson, who introduced me to The Four-Way Test, to join the board," added Brad. "Given her solid network of connections, she will be able to recommend other board members, too."

Brad trusted Andrea implicitly and could hardly wait to catch up with her in person. More than anything else, however, he needed Andrea to help him understand why Sally had cut off all contact with him.

14

The Mentor

Hearing his typical three knocks on her office door, Andrea looked up from her desk. "Come on in, Brad. It is great to see you. How's it going?"

Andrea had been following Brad's business growth in media reports and was a regular listener of his podcast. She expected him to be euphoric, but his demeanor suggested otherwise.

"It's nice to see you, too," replied Brad. "Things are going great with All Good. Bringing Ravi on board is the best thing that I've done for the success of the business.

"I wish I could say the same about my personal life, though," he added glumly. He went on to explain that Sally had refused to respond to any of his phone calls, texts, or emails.

"I really wish that there was something that I could do," responded Andrea. "But clearly, you remind her of her father and his problems with the law. I hate to say it, but she might never change her mind about you."

Brad sighed. "I get it. But I'm not ready to give up."

Andrea smiled. "I admire your commitment, Brad.

I've got my fingers crossed for you. As for Sally, give her some time to sort things out."

"You're right," said Brad before steering the conversation in a different direction. "The reason that I am here is that Ravi and I would like to have you as the first member of All Good's board of advisors."

Honored, Andrea readily agreed.

"That's great!" exclaimed Brad. "I'm hoping that you can recommend a few other candidates, too. We need people of high moral character who can keep us focused on building a business in alignment with The Four-Way Test," said Brad, nodding toward the framed edition of the document that had inspired his commitment.

"I'm up for the challenge. In fact, I know some great potential board members who will be nearby in about an hour. Care to meet some of them today?" asked Andrea.

"Sure," said Brad without hesitation.

Andrea and Brad walked the block from her office to the upscale luxury hotel where the Downtown Rotary Club had been meeting for more than seventy years. Riding with them in the elevator to the third-floor banquet hall were men and women of different ages and races. Their conversations about recent Rotary service projects impressed Brad.

A pair of club ambassadors stationed at the front door of the banquet room greeted Andrea and Brad with an enthusiastic welcome. A group of smiling Rotarians sitting at a round table at the front of the room waved at them and made a beckoning gesture with their hands.

"That's my father and some of his buddies," Andrea said to Brad. "Let's join them for lunch."

Brad was surprised that every person at the table stood up to introduce him or herself with a handshake. "Very old-school," thought Brad. Out of the corner of his eye, he spotted a banner featuring The Four-Way Test on the stage next to the podium. He wondered if the universe was trying to tell him something.

The lunchtime conversation was livelier and more energetic than Brad had expected. As a young man, he had attended Rotary meetings as a guest of his grandfather's, the same one who had visited him in his dream. He remembered people as being very welcoming and kind. But while his grandfather's club was made up almost exclusively of old white men, Andrea's Rotary club was more dynamic and diverse—a welcome and exciting change.

Soon, the president of the club called the meeting to order. For the next hour, she presided over an agenda that spotlighted local causes that the club supported. The weekly speaker was the executive director of the local children's museum, who explained how a grant from the club had made the playground accessible to hundreds of wheelchair-dependent kids.

"I promised to introduce you to some interesting people and prospective board members," said Andrea to Brad after the club president rang the bell to adjourn the meeting.

She guided him to the other side of the room. "Brad, meet my good friend Anthony Sanderson. He has built a fabulous community of people who share a love for sailing and who meet weekly at Anthony's sailing club for a group sail."

"Terrific to meet you, Brad." Anthony's smile was wide below his bushy mustache. "Andrea has told me all about your shoe company, and I love what you're doing. I remember seeing so much poverty in Brazil when I went there to pick up a sailboat for a client. It's tremendous that you've found a way to help."

Anthony continued, "How about coming to my sailing club tonight to join me and some of our members for our weekly Wednesday Night Sail? I'd love to get to know you better, and I'm sure my members would, too!"

"I've never sailed before," said Brad. "But I've always wanted to. Count me in."

15

Truthful Sailing

A few hours after the Rotary meeting, Anthony received an email message from Andrea.

Anthony,

Thank you for being so hospitable to my friend Brad Parsons at today's Rotary meeting. I appreciate your offer to have him join you for tonight's Wednesday Night Sail. I wish I could be there, but I know that Brad will be in good hands.

He is interested in applying The Four-Way Test to all aspects of his business. Would you be willing to share your business-origin story with him? It is a wonderful example of the first part (Is it the truth?) and a lesson he can use as he grows his business.
Your friend,
Andrea

Anthony smiled at Andrea's creativity. He was happy to share his story and participate in Brad's education.

That evening, as Brad pulled up in front of the sailing club, he saw Anthony standing outside. He was chatting and laughing with three of his members. Anthony waved Brad into a parking spot.

"Welcome!" he boomed as Brad got out of his car. "Let's walk around the marina a bit before folks start arriving for tonight's sail."

"Sounds great," replied Brad. "It'll give me the chance to check things out. I don't know the marina area very well."

"Walking is my main form of exercise these days," said Anthony as they strolled along the promenade with its view of the bay. "It's also how I stay on top of what's happening with my business." He went on to describe how he went on at least two long marina walks a year with each of his sixty-five employees.

"That's a lot of walks," marveled Brad. "Why so many?"

"When I ask employees in staff meetings how things are going, they say 'fine,'" replied Anthony. "People don't want to complain in front of their peers or supervisors. But when I speak with people one-on-one, they are more open. They're not afraid to express their opinions about the business or share the challenges that they're facing."

"Getting at the truth is something I've struggled with in my current and previous companies," admitted Brad. "I can see why your walks are so effective."

Anthony nodded. "Hearing the truth and telling the truth are critical to business success. When I started the sailing school twenty-five years ago, I was so broke that I had to borrow a boat to teach lessons. To save money, I lived in my van near the docks. I would drive away and pull into the parking lot at the same time as my sailing students because I was convinced that nobody wanted to take lessons from a guy living in an old van.

"One day I overslept and woke up to the sound of two of my students tapping on the windshield," he continued. "They said they envied my carefree lifestyle and beautiful ocean views—and pretty soon everybody knew the truth."

"That doesn't sound like a big deal to me," said Brad.

"My students felt the same way," said Anthony. "I could have avoided a lot of emotional stress if I had told the truth from the very beginning. But I learned an important lesson: Being truthful might seem scary, but it is a much easier way to live. The truth will set you up for success."

Anthony went on to describe how word about his dedication to his business got out, drawing attention from the media, and bringing in new students who helped grow his business into one of the largest and most successful sailing schools of its kind.

That evening, Brad watched with wonder as Anthony expertly navigated the twenty-four-foot sailboat across the bay. He engaged naturally with everyone—treating all on board not just as clients, but also as friends.

Brad stared out at the water and wondered how he might use truthfulness to build strong relationships and grow his company.

16

The Real Cause

Can you meet me at the office at 7 a.m. tomorrow before the rest of the team arrives?

Brad's cryptic text arrived just as Ravi was getting ready to go to bed. Had Brad gotten into some sort of trouble again? Ravi woke up four or five times that night thinking about worst-case scenarios.

The next morning, Ravi walked into Brad's office and found him sitting at his desk slowly turning the pages of a yellowed photo album.

"Good morning," said Ravi. "What's going on?"

Brad motioned for Ravi to sit down. "Take a look at these," he replied. "My mom took these photos with a cheap camera that my father had left behind. Those were rough years for us. She struggled to pay rent and put food on the table with the little that she earned working at the grocery store."

Ravi knew that Brad had come from a modest family but had no idea that their living conditions had been so precarious.

"One of the reasons I started All Good was to give people a chance to make a decent living," continued Brad. "Until last night, I never wanted to share my personal connection to poverty because I was embarrassed. But I met an amazing entrepreneur who made me realize how shortsighted I was to avoid opportunities to hear and tell the truth."

As Ravi listened, he felt a flush of relief. He realized that Brad's reason for starting All Good should be reflected in the company's actions.

"We've been talking about promoting economic development by offering low-skilled workers a good wage, job training, and opportunities for advancement," said Ravi excitedly. "But we can do much better than that."

"Go on," prompted Brad.

"Look, we enjoy a generous profit margin. I think we can afford to give away one free pair of sandals to someone in need for every pair we sell."

Over the next few days, Brad and Ravi pored over the company's financials. With the feasibility of a buy one, give one, or BOGO, program firmly established, the marketing team quickly went to work.

Within a week, All Good released its first commercial. Standing in the run-down courtyard of his old middle school, Brad shared the story of how kids had made fun of him because of his secondhand shoes, which were all that his mother could afford. He spoke with pride about All Good's commitment to providing a free pair of sandals to a needy child for every pair sold.

Almost overnight, All Good's sales took off. Consumers embraced the company for its values, and employee morale rose. The BOGO's halo effect made it easier to recruit new employees for the growing company. Being truthful about his background created an opportunity much larger than Brad could have ever imagined.

17

Ready to Join

"It's great to see you back, Brad," welcomed Andrea, who was standing by the front door of the hotel ballroom as an official greeter for the Downtown Rotary Club meeting.

"I'm so grateful for the introduction to Anthony," replied Brad. "His advice has been transformative for me and my business. And guess what? I've officially become a member of your club. I'm looking forward to getting more involved and meeting more interesting people."

"Fantastic!" exclaimed Andrea. "Speaking of interesting people, you should definitely sit at my table today since I've invited Mike Samuels to join me. Mike has built a thriving personal injury legal practice and credits much of his success to The Four-Way Test."

Andrea and Brad walked together to the buffet line. The hotel's catering department had outdone itself with a delectable offering of fried chicken, potato salad, and green beans. After filling their plates, they sat down at a table where Mike was already seated and eating his lunch.

"Good afternoon, Mike," said Andrea. "Let me introduce you to our club's newest member, Brad Parsons."

"Nice to meet you, Brad," said Mike, standing up to shake Brad's hand. "How did you find out about Rotary?"

"Well, my grandfather was a Rotarian, and I went to a few meetings with him growing up. To be honest, I had completely forgotten about Rotary until I met Andrea. Thanks to her, I've experienced the value of Rotary and knew that I had to join."

Brad shared with Mike his story about spending time with Anthony Sanderson.

"Anthony is a terrific guy who serves our club in so many ways." Mike smiled. "We have many members who you'll enjoy meeting. In fact, I suggest that you join our Ambassador Committee. It's a great way to meet people since you'll get to stand at the front door greeting them as they arrive."

Andrea laughed. "I've got to hand it to you, Mike. It's Brad's first meeting as a member, and you're already recruiting him to your committee. Well played."

"You know me, there's no time to delay when it comes to getting new members involved," Mike smiled. "Speaking of which, Brad, if you are free right after this meeting, why don't you join me for a home visit? I am going out to see a woman who applied for a free motorized scooter through the Wheels of Power Committee that I chair. It would be a wonderful opportunity for you to see one of the best things that our club does."

"You're something else, Mike," said Andrea chuckling.

"Well, my afternoon meeting cancelled so I'd be glad to join you," said Brad with enthusiasm.

In the car heading to the east side of town, Brad asked, "Mike, how long have you been a member of Downtown Rotary?"

"Twenty-two years," replied Mike. "But it seems like much less than that. Time flies when you serve causes that you believe in—*and* when you get to do it alongside your friends."

As they drove through one of the city's poorer neighborhoods, Brad noticed billboards advertising similar services: bail bonds, used cars, low-cost car insurance, worker's compensation, and personal injury legal representation.

"Mike, I haven't seen billboards from your personal injury law firm. Why aren't you advertising when your competitors are?" asked Brad.

"Great question," responded Mike. "It's one that I get a lot. But here's the thing: most of the companies that advertise are more concerned about selling their products and services than serving the community.

"I take a different approach to building relationships and growing my practice, thanks to some great mentors who've taught me the value of the second part of The Four-Way Test."

Mike continued, "If you recall, it asks us to examine whether the things we think, say, or do are fair to all concerned. It wouldn't be fair for me to come into this neighborhood and not recognize that there is a need for basic items like food, housing, and medical items like wheelchairs."

Brad thought about Mike's words. "How long have you been serving on the Wheels of Power Committee?"

"About fifteen years," replied Mike. "I've met so many great people along the way, too."

"The world needs more altruists like you," said Brad.

"Well, I shouldn't be called an altruist."

"Why not?"

"More than half the clients for my personal injury law firm come from this neighborhood, even though I've never advertised," said Mike.

Brad was incredulous. "How can that be?"

"People prefer to do business with and refer business to people they know, like, and trust," said Mike. "My success is proof of that. A motorized scooter for someone who needs it does more to generate goodwill and build positive relationships than any amount of slick advertising. And there is nothing in the world that beats the feeling I get from making a difference in other people's lives."

Brad nodded his head in agreement. His mind raced as he thought about ways to apply Mike's wisdom in his own life.

18

Overcoming Resistance

Waking at the crack of dawn, Brad found it impossible to go back to sleep. Anxiety washed over him as he thought about the first meeting of his company's board of advisors, which was scheduled for later that morning.

After much tossing and turning, he got out of bed and decided on a thirty-minute guided meditation to calm his nerves and focus his attention. Practicing a series of breathing exercises, Brad felt his anxiety melt away. Suddenly, his vibrating phone pulled him out of his reverie.

"I'm sorry to call you this early." Ravi sounded concerned. "But I wanted to give you a heads-up before your meeting with the board."

"It's okay, I've been awake for a while," said Brad. "What's up?"

Ravi continued, "Last night I got a long text from Ian Donnelly. He is irate about the resources we are putting into the BOGO program. He wants to know why we are wasting investor money on something that is not guaranteed to benefit the bottom line.'"

Brad's heart rate quickened and sweat began to bead on his forehead. He paused for a moment, remembering his meditation class, and took a long, deep breath. Slowly, he exhaled.

"Are you okay?" asked Ravi.

"I'm fine," Brad answered, even though he felt a knot growing in his stomach. "I appreciate the notice. I'll see you at the office."

Ravi was worried. Brad's behavior had changed so much over the past few months that Ravi was not sure what to expect from his friend anymore. Brad was worried, too. What if the other board members shared the same concerns as Ian?

Brad thought back to his own childhood and how he had felt when his mother could not afford to buy him new shoes. The BOGO program was an expense that most companies would not willingly incur—and it was one that Brad was adamant about not giving up.

Arriving at All Good's headquarters without a moment to spare, Brad walked into the conference room where Ravi and the other board members were already waiting. Brad began with an update on the privately held company's finances, including its 85 percent year-over-year growth rate and its inclusion on various media lists of fastest-growing companies. Except for Ian, the other board members smiled and nodded their heads in approval.

His presentation complete, Brad opened the meeting up to questions. Ravi held his breath, wondering how Brad would deal with criticism of the BOGO program.

"The top-line sales numbers are great," began Ian. "But there is not nearly enough dropping to the bottom line because the company is giving away too much free product."

Brad took a deep breath. Calmly, he asked, "What do you think we should do, Ian?"

Ian responded without hesitation. "Significantly scale back or curtail the BOGO program entirely."

"Look," said Brad, passion rising in his voice. "I understand that we need to watch our costs. Too many start-ups spend their money before growing their revenue stream. But the BOGO program is core to my personal values, and it satisfies an important need that no other company addresses. It is not fair to the people we serve to cut it back. That said, we can and should find other ways to save money."

Brad was ready for Ian to push back. In his mind, he had already rehearsed how to respond. But much to Brad's surprise, Ian backed down. Instead, Ian led the board in a forty-five-minute discussion about ways to reduce other business costs while continuing the BOGO program.

19

Prosperity Rising

Six months after the board of advisors meeting, All Good was decidedly in the black. Brad's personal story was a mainstay of the media, and he became a frequent guest of morning television programs. With celebrities and fashion influencers buzzing about how much they loved their sandals, it did not take long for other companies to emulate All Good's example of giving back.

The extraordinary success of the BOGO program and its contribution to All Good's growth made Brad feel vindicated. More importantly, the positive publicity caught the attention of the two people most important to him.

Brad had not seen or heard from his mother since storming out of her trailer. So, he was surprised to pick up the phone on a Friday afternoon and hear Sandra Parson's voice.

She spoke softly. "I saw you on television when I got home from work yesterday. When you talked about how we couldn't afford new shoes for you when you were a kid, I cried. I still feel bad about that—and I'm so proud of what you are doing to make things better for folks who need help."

"Thanks, Mom." Brad choked up for a moment before continuing. "I probably should have checked with you before sharing our family story on national TV. I'm sorry if I embarrassed you."

"Honey, there's no need to apologize," replied Sandra. "What you are doing is wonderful, and I am the proudest mother in the world."

Later that same day, Brad received an unexpected text from Sally.

Congratulations on your profile in this month's business journal. You are doing amazing work.

Brad had been sure that he would never hear from Sally again. Not wanting to waste a precious second, he responded immediately.

Fantastic hearing from you, Sally. Can we talk?

Brad's smartphone vibrated moments later. Accepting the video conference request, he came face to face with Sally's beaming smile and beautiful eyes. Without thinking, he blurted out, "I missed you."

Brad and Sally soon fell back into the easy rapport they had when they were first getting to know one another. Only now, Brad was not restricted to home confinement. A week later, they went to dinner at Sally's favorite Italian restaurant, and Brad could not believe his good fortune when, at the end of the evening, Sally agreed to date him. Never had things worked out so well for him both personally and professionally.

Naturally, Brad called Andrea to share the good news and to thank her for introducing him to the mentors responsible for helping him turn his life and business around.

"I'm thrilled for you, Brad," said Andrea. "How else can I help?"

"Well, I'm dealing with something that is new to me," said Brad with a chuckle. "For the first time, I'm putting money into savings and I need a financial advisor. You must know someone you can recommend."

20

Goodwill and Friendship First

B rad thought that the name Albert Cheevers sounded familiar, but he couldn't quite place it. When his car's GPS announced that he had arrived at Cheevers Center, he had to smile. He wondered why Andrea had not told him that she was introducing him to the president of Cheevers Capital Management and a member of the Downtown Rotary Club.

Finding street parking a few blocks away, Brad walked toward the tallest building in town. He looked up at the sleek fifty-story glass office building with its green-tinted windows and admired how the structure swept up to a triangular point like a pyramid. He had always admired the stunning architecture and was excited about going inside for the first time.

The lobby with its black marble floors, white leather seating, and pieces of modern art made an immediate impression for its understated elegance. Brad entered the elevator reserved for the upper floors where Cheevers Capital Management was located.

The rapid ascent gave Brad just enough time to watch the thirty-second video playing on a big screen on the elevator's back wall. It highlighted the work of the Cheever Charitable Foundation to provide recreational and educational opportunities for area youth over the past fifty years.

When the elevator doors opened, Brad faced a smiling receptionist seated behind a futuristic glass and stainless-steel desk. "Welcome, Mr. Parsons," she said as she directed him toward a set of tall red double doors. "Mr. Cheevers is expecting you."

Pushing the doors open, Brad saw a tall, slender man in his late sixties or early seventies putting a golf ball across a small artificial turf that ran next to the office's floor-to-ceiling windows.

"Hello, Brad," greeted Albert in a friendly voice. He motioned toward two modern black leather sofas facing one another in the middle of the room. "I appreciate your taking the time to come downtown to visit. I have heard great things about you from Andrea. Anybody she recommends is somebody I'm excited to meet."

"So, do you play a lot of golf?" asked Brad.

"I wish I could say yes, but I'm so busy with the company and our foundation that I don't play as often as I would like," replied Albert.

"I know the feeling," said Brad. "I played on the golf team in college and love the sport but haven't golfed in over a year."

"Well, today must be my lucky day." Albert gave Brad a wink. "Our foundation is holding a fundraising event next month, and it would be great to have you join my group to tilt things in our favor. All the money we raise goes directly to our youth programs."

Brad said, "That sounds like a lot of fun and a great cause. I appreciate the vote of confidence in my rusty golf skills. I would love to join your team. And I promise to practice a few rounds beforehand."

"Excellent! But enough about golf. How can I be of service to you, Brad?"

Brad explained that he was looking for a financial advisor to help him as he navigated All Good's rapid growth and financial success.

"I can certainly help you with that," Albert said. "But I need to get to know you better before I can refer you to the right advisor."

Brad nodded. "That makes sense. The third part of The Four-Way Test asks us to consider whether our thoughts, words, and actions promote goodwill and better friendships."

"I'm impressed," exclaimed Albert with raised eyebrows. "You've been in Rotary for a few months and are already quoting The Four-Way Test. Let me guess: Andrea turned you on to it?"

"You got it!" Brad laughed.

For the next hour, Albert asked Brad about his past and questioned him about his future dreams. Not once did he talk about himself or promote Cheevers Capital Management. Albert's easygoing and nonjudgmental demeanor reminded Brad of how his grandfather used to talk with him, and he knew that he would have faith in any financial advisor who Albert recommended.

21

A New Mindset

On the ten-minute drive to work, Brad thought about how far All Good had come in its relatively short history. While pleased with the company's growth, he could not help but be bothered by recent departures of a couple of key employees. The fact that they were in line for raises and promotions further confused him.

Deep in thought, Brad strode through the front door of the office and past receptionist Olive Taveres' desk. Olive was not surprised that he did not stop to say hello. She had learned that Brad was an intense boss who did not like to be distracted when he was preoccupied.

Heading straight to Ravi's office, he entered without knocking. "I keep turning something over in my head that maybe you can help me understand."

"Good morning to you, too!" joked Ravi.

"Oops, sorry," replied Brad. "It's just that there is no time for small talk when we have important issues to deal with."

"Wait a second," countered Ravi. "Small talk *is* important. It can be the difference between developing rapport and trust—or not."

Having made his point, Ravi listened as Brad described his concerns about the employees who had departed. Like Brad, Ravi was worried about turnover. It was difficult and expensive to find and train good team members, and the company needed to do a much better job of hanging on to them.

"I believe the problem is related to the small-talk issue we just discussed," said Ravi.

"I don't get it." Brad looked confused.

Ravi said, "In exit interviews and on job boards, employees say that they love our products and the company mission. But they don't feel like senior management is interested in getting to know them or hearing their ideas.

"Look, we have great employees, and we pay them well," continued Ravi. "But we need to take the time to listen to them. We also need to create opportunities for them to share their thoughts and interact with each other outside the office. I'm sure that they have ideas for improving the business to make us more creative and efficient—and profitable."

Brad was quiet for a few moments as he considered Ravi's words. "I see where you are coming from," he finally said. "Your advice reminds me of a conversation that I had about the importance of building goodwill and friendships. How do you think we should do this?"

Ravi beamed. He was thrilled with the direction of the conversation, as he had tried in the past to engage Brad about improving the workplace environment to no avail. Until now, Brad had been more interested in discussing bottom-line details.

"Let's meet for dinner tonight," suggested Ravi. "I have some ideas I'd like to share with you about improving the company culture. How about sushi at your favorite downtown spot?"

"You got it. I'll make a 7 p.m. reservation at Hiroshi's."

Returning to his desk, Ravi opened a document on his computer that he had started several months ago but never finished. He knew that dinner with Brad was his chance to share his ideas for improving All Good's company culture, and he immediately got to work.

Ravi arrived at the restaurant to find Brad already there. Sitting cross-legged on a tatami mat in a small private room, Brad motioned for Ravi to join him.

"I hope you are hungry; I've ordered a lot of sushi for us," said Brad. "How about sharing your ideas while we enjoy some edamame?"

Taking a deep breath, Ravi pulled a ten-page document out of his black leather backpack.

"I came up with a list," said Ravi with some trepidation. Ravi had admired Brad's confidence and take-charge nature ever since they had met in business school, but those attributes could also feel intimidating at times.

"Well, I know what I'll be reading this weekend." Brad laughed, which put Ravi at ease. "Before we dive into the particulars, what is it that we need to change?"

"It's really quite simple," replied Ravi. "We need to encourage our employees to share their ideas, and we need to implement those that will make our company better."

22

Shifting Fortunes

A few short months after Brad and Ravi's meeting over sushi, All Good was a better place to work. Instead of retreating into their offices, they and the rest of the management team made efforts to build stronger connections. They instituted a daily stand-up huddle, which became a chance for everyone to discuss priorities and celebrate shared wins.

Most notably, company leaders began scheduling one-on-one walking meetings with their team members in the park adjacent to All Good's building, a best practice that Brad had learned from sailing school owner and Rotarian Anthony Sanderson. To their surprise, managers found that people were more relaxed and willing to share ideas and discuss problems when they were away from the distractions of their colleagues, computers, and phones.

Team members were also encouraged to share their creativity and drop new product ideas, cost-saving suggestions, and workplace-improvement recommendations into whimsical mailboxes shaped like light bulbs, which were positioned throughout the office. Each week, Brad awarded the employee with the winning idea a $1,000 bonus and interviewed him or her for a segment on his podcast.

With morale and profitability at an all-time high, Brad impulsively decided to reward the entire company with a multiday retreat at a high-end beach resort in Baja California, Mexico. He saw it as a great opportunity to bond in a relaxed setting, and it was a significant departure from the past two years when only top managers were invited.

Sitting in a lounge chair on the balcony of his penthouse, Brad reflected on the upcoming trip and all the good things that had been happening. His business was making a difference in the world while generating its highest level of profits. His employee- and customer-satisfaction scores were the best that they had ever been. Life seemed perfect.

Then, his cell phone vibrated with an incoming text from Sally.

Brad, are you free now? We need to talk.

Worried, Brad called back immediately. "Is everything all right, Sally?"

"No," said Sally curtly.

"What's up?" asked Brad.

"I've seen you once this month," replied Sally. "And next week, you are leaving for Mexico when you promised to come to the charity auction that I've spent the last few months putting together."

"I'm really sorry," said Brad. "I know that I've been obsessed with the business. But I promise that things have calmed down and that we'll have much more time to spend together when I get back from Mexico."

"I've heard that before, Brad," said Sally. "I think it's best that we go our own ways so we can focus on the things we value most."

"You don't understand, Sally. You *are* important to me. Please give me another chance," implored Brad.

"I'm done," said Sally firmly. "I don't trust your promises anymore." Then, she hung up.

For the next week, Brad called, texted, and emailed Sally, who simply ignored him. Not even a few days in Mexico could pull him out of his funk, and he returned feeling lonelier than ever.

Depressed, Brad called Andrea for advice.

"I'm not the best person to help you," said Andrea. "Fortunately, I know somebody who is: my dad, Robert."

23

Benefiting All

Brad had talked with Robert, a fellow member of the Downtown Rotary Club, on just a few occasions. They had never spoken for any great length of time, however, since Robert had many friends in the club with whom he socialized.

So, it was with great curiosity that Brad stood in the sleek glassed-in lobby of his loft building at 4:30 a.m., waiting for Robert to arrive. Exhausted from long days of work, Brad was on his third cup of coffee when a large forest-green SUV pulled up to the front of the building and jolted him alert with three short honks.

Brad jogged out to the vehicle and loaded a duffel bag containing his fly-fishing gear into the back seat. As soon as Brad swung open the front passenger door, Robert greeted him with a beaming smile.

"Morning, Brad. A great day to be alive, right? I've been looking forward to this all week."

"Me, too," responded Brad, even though he had never been much of a fisherman.

"It will take about an hour and a half to drive to my secret fishing spot."

"That's great, because I have a lot of questions for you." Brad suddenly felt energized thanks to Robert's enthusiasm.

Robert encouraged Brad as they made their way onto the highway. "Go ahead, ask away."

"Well, until just a few weeks ago, I felt like my life was perfect." He went on to explain how excited he was to be making a difference in the world and to see his employees happier and more engaged than ever.

"Sounds like the perfect situation," said Robert.

"I thought so, too," agreed Brad. "Then a couple of weeks ago, my girlfriend, Sally, said that we should stop seeing each other because she feels like I'm ignoring her. But—"

"Wait a second," interrupted Robert. "Is she right?"

"No, she means the world to me," Brad answered without hesitation.

"Then, why doesn't she know it?" asked Robert.

Brad looked sheepish. "Well, I guess I've been so laser focused on growing my company that I haven't spent much time with her."

"I know how that goes," said Robert. "When I was trying to save my insurance company from going under, I thought that I needed to spend all my time working.

Fortunately, our mutual friend Albert Cheevers reminded me about the importance of personal relationships."

Robert continued, "Albert's wisdom changed my life. He made me realize that my obsession with work was not benefiting my wife, Marion. Even when we were together, I was so wrapped up thinking about the business that I didn't focus on what she was saying and feeling."

"Well, I'm assuming that you changed your ways, because Andrea told me that you and your wife have been together for thirty-five years," said Brad.

Robert nodded his head. "I did. I discovered that the key to maintaining a great relationship is to make it a priority. I also try to follow the last part of The Four-Way Test. I always try to make sure that the things I think, say, and do are beneficial to all concerned, which certainly includes those closest to me."

Robert went on to detail his standing Friday-night date with his wife, Marion. "Sometimes, we go out to eat. Other times we cook a nice meal together. During the summer, we sit in the backyard after dinner and look up at the stars through the branches of our large trees.

"What we do on date night is much less important than the attitude I bring to the evening," added Robert, explaining how he made a conscientious effort not to talk over his wife and to listen closely as she spoke.

"I can relate," replied Brad. "I tend to dominate conversations, especially when I'm excited about an idea. Do you have any other tips?"

"Well, I never share my opinions with other people before asking them at least three questions and listening carefully to what they say," said Robert. "I'd be lying if I said that I always succeed at doing this, but I have become better at understanding other people's points of view."

"I love it! Any other great relationship-building ideas?" asked Brad.

"Actually, three more," replied Robert. "First, ask people about their dreams and do what you can to help make them happen. Second, praise people publicly and offer constructive advice in private. Third, surprise people in positive ways that are meaningful to them."

"This is tremendous," said Brad. "I wish I could repay you somehow."

"Well, you can," said Robert. "Bill Evers is a member of our Rotary club, and his son—who is graduating with an MBA from your alma mater—is looking for a position with a socially responsible company. I thought he might be able to interview at your company."

"I'll make it happen."

"Excellent!" Robert turned off the highway and onto a bumpy gravel road. A few minutes later, he pulled over to the side of the road that ran next to a creek. "We're here. Ready to land some monster trout?"

"That would be the icing on the cake," said Brad. "This has already been the most successful fishing trip of my life."

24

Balance

Andrea waited in her favorite coffee shop with its midcentury interior design and jazz playlist streaming in the background. Brad had requested the meeting with a text announcing that he had big news to share.

As Andrea sipped her coffee and caught up on email, Brad slipped into the recliner across from her.

"How's my guide doing?"

Startled, Andrea answered, "Hey Brad. Great to see you. Did you just call me your guide?"

"I sure did," replied Brad.

"What do you mean by that?" asked Andrea.

"Well, the first time I met you, you gave me a coffee mug emblazoned with The Four-Way Test on it," said Brad. "Your advice and the people you've introduced me to have made such a huge impact on my life."

Andrea was flattered. "That is great to hear, Brad. But offering advice is easy. Following through is the hard part—and I admire the work you've put into improving yourself.

"Speaking of improvements," continued Andrea, "I talked to Sally a few days ago, and she told me that you two are back together. She seems really happy, too. Whatever you are doing, keep it up."

Brad shared with Andrea the relationship advice that her father, Robert, had given him and which he had taken to heart.

"I'm not surprised." Andrea laughed. "My dad learned from the smartest teacher I know: my mom."

"I guess Sally didn't tell you the best part?" asked Brad.

"Oh, and what's that?"

Brad grinned. "I proposed last weekend . . . and she said yes!" He described taking Sally to meet his mother and how Sandra and Sally hit it off right away.

"I hadn't visited my mom in a very long time. I was always using work as an excuse, but your father helped me understand that I need to make time for my relationships."

Andrea congratulated Brad on his good news and promised to stop by Sally's office that afternoon to deliver her well wishes in person.

"She would love that," responded Brad.

Later that evening as Brad was getting ready for bed, he reached into his cabinet and took out the coffee mug that Andrea had given him. Sipping on a cup of chamomile tea to help him sleep, he reread The Four-

Way Test and fully appreciated the simplicity and power of its twenty-four words.

That night, as he slept, his grandfather reappeared in a dream.

> *"I've missed you!" shouted Brad, looking up at his grandfather, who was again perched on the lip of a giant version of the mug that he had used that evening.*
>
> *"I've missed you, too," replied his grandfather.*
>
> *"Did you know that I've been learning to live by The Four-Way Test?" inquired Brad.*
>
> *"Of course, I've been watching," said his grandfather. "I'm so proud that you are putting the words into practice. Too many people fail to recognize and act on their wisdom."*

Before Brad had a chance to respond, his alarm rang, and he opened his eyes.

25

Pay It Forward

Brad looked at his calendar and saw that Jeff Evers, the job candidate whom Robert Hanson had recommended, was scheduled to arrive at his office at 9 a.m. That would give Brad just enough time to attend that morning's team huddle with the production and accounting teams.

By making regular attendance at team meetings a priority, Brad and the other All Good executives had shown their commitment to building friendships and goodwill. The huddles were a chance for employees to ask questions and talk openly and honestly about the opportunities and challenges they faced. Morale was improving, and team members felt like they were being heard and their ideas were being implemented.

Fifteen minutes before Jeff arrived for his interview, Brad reviewed the evaluation forms from the three team members who had already spoken with him. Their feedback was consistent: Jeff was intelligent, articulate, and he demonstrated great knowledge about socially responsible enterprises in general and All Good in particular.

However, Brad was concerned that his colleagues wondered whether Jeff's confidence would interfere with his ability to be a team player. One supervisor wrote, "I'd be nervous having Jeff on my team. We have such outstanding rapport in my department that having somebody who thinks he's the smartest person in the room could change the collaborative dynamic we've developed."

Brad's phone buzzed with a notification that Jeff had arrived and was waiting in the lobby. Brad texted in return.

Please send him back.

Moments later, Jeff—a tall, muscular blond twenty-four-year-old—appeared outside of Brad's glass door. He looked a lot like Brad and carried himself with the same cockiness that Brad remembered having as a newly minted MBA.

"I've been looking forward to meeting you, Mr. Parsons," said Jeff. "I've heard great things about you and All Good."

"That's wonderful," said Brad. "Aside from the interviews we've put you through, what's keeping you busy these days?"

With pride in his voice, Jeff replied, "Well, I'm leading a team that will be presenting for the business school's Entrepreneurial Challenge next week. We're confident that we can win."

Brad smiled, thinking about his participation in the same competition not that long ago. Jeff reminded him of a former version of himself.

"I admire your confidence," replied Brad. "How did you enjoy your interviews with my colleagues?"

Jeff said, "I learned a lot from each one. Your company is doing so many terrific things, and I can't imagine a better place to work."

"So, what other questions do you have about the company?" asked Brad.

"I'm curious to learn how you've built such a cohesive team. Every person I've interviewed with is committed to All Good's mission. I even spoke to some of your customers, and they feel the same way."

"I'm happy to hear that." Brad smiled. "But it didn't happen overnight. Things really changed when we started following The Four-Way Test." Brad pointed to the document in the gold frame that hung on the wall behind his chair.

Jeff read the document. "Those are amazingly simple rules and seem quite sensible. I'm surprised that none of my professors ever talked about them in business school."

"The principles have been around since 1932," said Brad. "Unfortunately, people often overlook them, unable to believe that such simple rules can be effective in a complex world."

"Well, based on your success, they are rules I need to know," replied Jeff.

"Knowing them is not enough," said Brad. "Living them is the key. If I were to offer you a job, would you agree to live by them?"

"Yes, I would," said Jeff without hesitation.

Brad smiled. "Well, in that case, I'm pleased to welcome you to the All Good team . . . with one important caveat."

"What's that?" asked Jeff.

"I ask all new employees to share The Four-Way Test to make their lives, and the lives of others, better."

"I can't wait to get started."

Author's Note

THE FOUR-WAY TEST
of the things we think, say, or do

1. Is it the TRUTH?
2. Is it FAIR to all concerned?
3. Will it build GOODWILL and BETTER FRIENDSHIPS?
4. Will it be BENEFICIAL to all concerned?

Eloquent and simple, The Four-Way Test has guided people's thoughts and actions since the 1930s. Appearing on banners, plaques, mugs, magazines, and websites, these twenty-four words have become synonymous with Rotary International, one of the largest service organizations in the world.

The first time I had heard about The Four-Way Test was in 1988. I was doing postgraduate work at the University of São Paulo, Brazil, thanks to a generous

Rotary International Ambassadorial Scholarship. But it was not until many years later, after I had started my own business and joined the Rotary Club of Portland, Oregon, that I became curious about the origins of the four powerful principles that Herbert J. Taylor first drafted in 1932.

Taylor passed away in 1978, but a first-person account of his creation of The Four-Way Test can be found in his autobiography *The Herbert J. Taylor Story*.[2] As he tells it, Taylor was just thirty-seven years old when creditors from the Continental National Bank in Chicago, impressed with his performance at the Jewel Tea Company, asked him to split his time between the Jewel Tea Company and another Chicago-based company, Club Aluminum Products Company. With permission from Jewel Tea, Taylor agreed.

Tasked with keeping the Club Aluminum Products Company afloat and preserving the jobs of 250 employees, Taylor got to work. He soon discovered that things were even worse than he had imagined: the company faced a mountain of lawsuits and was $400,000 in debt (a hefty sum at that time). And yet, Taylor felt a higher calling. In 1932, in the depths of the Great Depression, Taylor resigned from his well-paying job at Jewel Tea, borrowed $6,100 against his Jewel Tea stock to cover operating

---

2   Herbert J. Taylor, *The Herbert J. Taylor Story* (Downers Grove, Illinois: InterVarsity Press, 1968).

costs, and became president of Club Aluminum at a salary of $6,000 a year.

One of the first things on Taylor's agenda was to create a code of conduct that everyone in the company could remember and follow. As he tells it, "I leaned over my desk, rested my head in my hands, and prayed. After a few moments, I looked up and reached for a white paper card. Then I wrote down the twenty-four words that had come to me. . . . I called it 'The Four-Way Test' of the things we think, say or do."[3]

That same day, Taylor began applying the test. One of the first things to cross his desk was an advertising tear sheet that promoted Club Aluminum's products as the greatest cookware in the world. Using the first question, "Is it the truth?" as his guide, he instructed his advertising manager to remove all unsubstantiated claims and stick to the facts in future advertisements.

On another occasion, a customer was prepared to place an order for more than fifty thousand utensils—a potential lifesaver for the company, which was still struggling to emerge from bankruptcy. The hitch? The customer intended to sell the products at cut-rate prices. As difficult as the decision was, Club Aluminum turned down the order because it was not fair to its regular dealers, who had been advertising and promoting Club

---

3   Taylor, *The Herbert J. Taylor Story*, 41.

Aluminum's products at a price that had been agreed upon as beneficial to all.

Over the next few weeks, Taylor applied the test to a variety of business problems and situations. A devout Christian, Taylor wanted The Four-Way Test to appeal to people of *all* faiths and backgrounds. Thus, two months after its creation, he called in his four department heads—each from a different religious background—and asked them if there was anything in The Four-Way Test that was contrary to their religious or moral beliefs. They answered no, and the Club Aluminum Products Company formally adopted The Four-Way Test.

The rest is history. Five years later, Club Aluminum paid off its debt and returned to profitability. During the next fifteen years, the company distributed over $1 million in stock dividends—and the only money that it borrowed or invested during that twenty-year span was the $6,100 that Taylor had brought with him when he joined the company.

Taylor credited the turnaround of Club Aluminum to The Four-Way Test and was happy to share it with others. In 1943, Rotary International adopted the test to promote its commitment to high ethical standards. In 1954, during Taylor's term as president of Rotary International, he presented the organization with the copyright.

Now in the public domain, companies and communities worldwide have adopted The Four-Way Test and translated it into the languages of more than a hundred countries. While some say it is overly simplistic, the test is powerful *because of its simplicity.* Rather than provide answers, it encourages creative problem solving and expansive thinking. To quote Herbert J. Taylor, "If the people who worked for Club Aluminum were to *think right,* I knew they would *do right.*"[4]

The beauty of Taylor's legacy is that it lives on, not just in business but also in government, in high school classrooms, and on the athletic playing field. It has inspired campaigns to promote safe driving, fire prevention, and crime reduction. Look hard enough during your travels, and you will find The Four-Way Test engraved on monuments and plaques in cities around the world.

My hope is that this book reminds us that civility and good decision making do not require a multipage statement of ethics that a team of lawyers drafts. All it takes is a desire to do the right thing and a simple test that brings out the best in every person who uses it.

---

4   Taylor, *The Herbert J. Taylor Story*, 40.

Acknowledgments

Throughout my career, I have been fortunate to befriend talented businesspeople and all-around wonderful human beings who have taught me not only the value of developing trust but also how to become a trusted advisor. This book owes much to the collective wisdom of Casey Filburn, Lou Heckler, Michael Knouse, Dyana King, Graeme Newell, Kerrie Phipps, Brandt Hulse, Tammy Wittren, Mike Olden, Dave Carroll, Anthony Sandberg, Mike Faith, Paul Witkay, Bob Horn, Steve Stogner, Mickey Maloney, Sue Cassidy, Aaron Miller, Ken Larsen, Bob Rosson, Jeff Capen, Kevin Schmidt, Art Ciocca, Tim Murray, Jo-Ann Rose, João Moura, André Moura, Kellie Poulsen-Grill, Al Jubitz, Steve Watts, Bruce Frederick, and Kate Ertmann.

I feel lucky to have tremendous friends who have provided me with great counsel and encouragement. Thank you to Marty Duffy, Wade Freeman, Nathan Blain, Pere Prat, Eric Rothberg, and Mark Ungar.

My mastermind group colleagues Allison Clarke, Scott Crabtree, Steve Brown, Bill Conerly, and Cathey Armillas have been a valuable source of support in my speaking, writing, coaching, and business endeavors. I am particularly grateful for their generosity in sharing the lessons they've learned from their personal and professional experiences.

I deeply appreciate the advice that I received from my friends and bestselling authors Richard Fenton and Andrea Waltz, who helped shape the characters and plot of this book. Their book *Million Dollar Book Formula: How to Write a Short Book That Will Sell Forever* helped guide me, and I recommend it to any aspiring or seasoned author who wants to write a successful book.

Kari Filburn and Ranilo Cabo, thank you for your editing and design skills. The quality of your work is evident throughout these pages.

Mom, Dad, Martha, Jeff, Chris, Hillary, Marilyn, Renate, and Guenther, your love and support have made me a better person.

Above all, I never would have completed this book without the support and encouragement of my wife Ellen and daughter Anya. Ellen, your masterful editing made the characters and story come to life. Anya, your enthusiasm for life and your talent for making friends never cease to inspire me.

About the Author

Patrick Galvin is an accomplished speaker, coach, and author as well as a TEDx presenter and past president of the Oregon Chapter of the National Speakers Association. Patrick's first bestselling parable, *The Connector's Way: A Story About Building Business One Relationship at a Time*, is the story of an entrepreneur who uncovers powerful relationship-building secrets that help him transform his business from failure into success. The book is available worldwide in print, Kindle, and Audible formats.

Patrick is also the cofounder and chief galvanizer of The Galvanizing Group, a learning and development company in Portland, Oregon, that helps high-performance companies and teams galvanize repeat and referred business through better relationships. Applying the principles of *The Connector's Way* and *The Trusted Way*, The Galvanizing Group offers a systematic and measurable approach to business relationship building taught through innovative coaching, training, and online learning programs.

Patrick has an MBA in international marketing from Thunderbird, one of the world's top-ranked international business programs, and a BS in Foreign Service from Georgetown University. He received a Rotary International Ambassadorial Scholarship for postgraduate studies at the University of São Paulo, Brazil. In addition to his native English, he is fluent in Spanish and Portuguese.

Patrick is an active member of the Rotary Club of Portland, Oregon, which he joined in 2012. He has held various leadership positions, including president of the club's charitable trust and chair of the Membership Committee. In 2015, he was a featured speaker at the Rotary International Convention in São Paulo, Brazil.

Patrick, his wife, and their daughter live in the beautiful Pacific Northwest where they enjoy volunteer work and a variety of outdoor activities including hiking, biking, swimming, running, and camping.

Bring *The Trusted Way* to Your Company, Conference, or Event

What if everyone in your audience, at your company, or on your team became better at building strong relationships grounded in trust?

The Trusted Way is the creation of Patrick Galvin, a dynamic keynote presenter, TEDx speaker, and business coach who works with organizations across the globe. Patrick takes great pride in engaging audiences with fresh and practical material, and he tailors his message to meet the unique needs of every audience. After hundreds of appearances, he has never delivered the same program twice—and he has the enthusiastic testimonials to show for it.

For information on having Patrick work with your organization or to book Patrick to speak at your next meeting or event, call 503.249.8800 or visit www. patrickgalvin.com.

Made in the USA
Coppell, TX
10 June 2021

57198565R00069